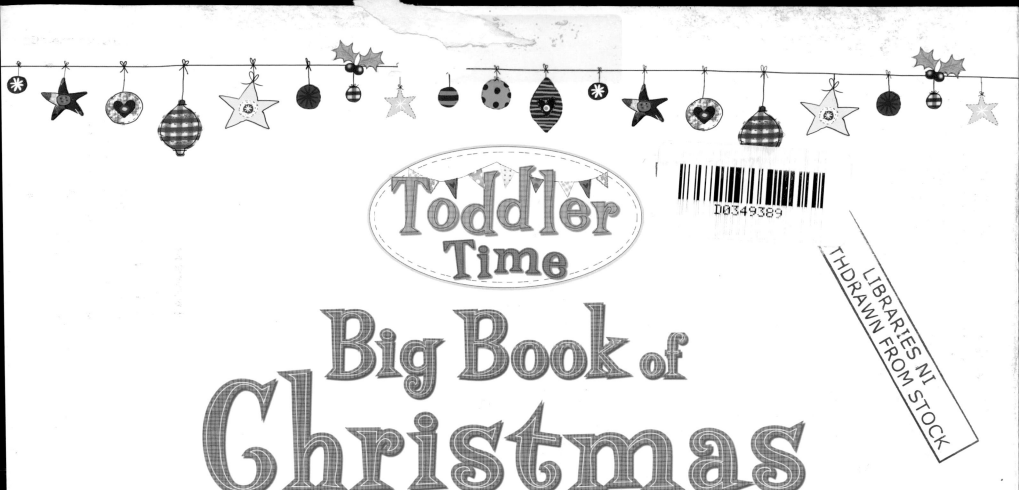

# Toddler Time
# Big Book of
# Christmas

Illustrated by Katie Saunders

nosy crow

# Notes to parents

**The Big Book of Christmas** provides the perfect mix of activities, information and stories to bring a little magic in the build-up to Christmas. Designed, illustrated and written by parents of toddlers, this beautifully illustrated collection has interactive questions throughout to engage all toddlers. It is divided into clear sections so you can dip in and out:

• **Christmas Games** are guaranteed to be a favourite. Encourage your toddler to study the pictures and give plenty of praise when they get the answer right. Don't feel you have to do the whole section in one go. When you have finished all the games, go back to the beginning as your toddler will love to show off!

• **Out and About** illustrates the magic of winter. This is an ideal opportunity to talk about the changing weather throughout the year and encourage your toddler to notice their surroundings.

• **Christmas Activities** provides suggestions for how to keep your toddler busy at this exciting time of year. You will have lots of fun together but please note all these activities will need adult help.

• **Learning Fun** takes a festive look at the all-important basic concepts of the alphabet, numbers, colours and shapes. This is a great way to increase your toddler's vocabulary, so take your time over this section and return to it often but take a break as soon as your toddler loses interest.

• **Stories and Songs** captures the essence of Christmas. This is your time to snuggle up with your toddler and enjoy the traditional side of the season with the story of *The First Christmas* and *The Nutcracker*. There's also the classic poem, *'Twas The Night Before Christmas* as well as a selection of favourite carols.

• **Christmas Quiz** is a collection of questions with a festive theme, perfectly chosen to build your toddler's confidence. Four separate sections test memory skills with the help of picture clues, so read each question carefully. Don't forget to be encouraging at all times and keep it light-hearted and fun.

# This book belongs to

...............................................

# Contents

# Christmas Games

Santa is sent lots of letters each year. Can you read this one?

Dear ,

I am sitting by the  looking out at the

. I am very excited about Christmas.

I have been a good  and hope you will bring

me some  in your . Please leave  for

my . I would love a  and a

for Christmas. My sister would like a

and a . I will leave a 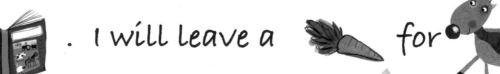 for

and a  for you by the . Love, Sam x

# Spot the Difference

## Can you find 6 missing things?

# Search and Find

Can you find these items? ⭐ elf without a hat ⭐ fairy doll

WOOD

⭐ sleeping elf  ⭐ tiger mask  ⭐ Santa's photo  ⭐ elves' cat

# Who's Been Here?

Who's been walking in the snow?

Can you make all the animal noises?

# Guess the Present

# Out and About

# I Spy

Join in a game of I SPY and see if you can find:

☆ robin ☆ berries ☆ squirrel ☆ icicle ☆ nuts ☆ window
☆ scarf ☆ mouse ☆ cobweb ☆ boot ☆ star

# Who's in the Park?

tree

deer

car

mouse

How many animals can you find?

gate

horse

swan

fox

bike

How can you tell it is cold in the park?

# Playing in the Snow

teddy bear

sledge

snowman

hat

scarf

dog

wellies

What do you like best about the snow?

# Christmas Activities

There's plenty for toddlers to do in each of these fun
activities but adult help is needed throughout.

# Letters to Santa

Santa loves to hear from all the children each year. Why don't you make a special envelope for your Christmas list and leave it out for him on Christmas Eve?

**Here's what you need:**
An envelope
Scissors
Craft glue
Glitter
Sequins
White card
Coloured pencils

And here's what you do:

1.  Write SANTA in big letters on the envelope using the craft glue then stick the sequins on.
2.  Draw a frame around the envelope using the glue then sprinkle glitter on and leave to dry.
3.  Draw colourful pictures of leaves and berries on your white card. Then ask an adult to cut them out.
4.  Stick your pictures on to your special envelope.

Don't forget to send a Thank You letter to Santa after Christmas. You can send this in another special envelope!

# Christmas Biscuits

Here are some very special biscuits that you can make just before Christmas.
You can choose which shape you would like. Here are some ideas to start you off:

⭐ Stockings    Presents    Snowmen    Reindeer    Stars    Christmas trees ⭐

**Here's what you need:**
280g plain flour
110g icing sugar (plus extra
 for the decoration)
55g ground almonds
140g butter
½ teaspoon vanilla essence
1 egg

## And here's what you do:

1.  Put flour, icing sugar and almonds in a bowl.
2.  Rub in butter until you have crumbs.
3.  Stir in vanilla, egg and 1-2 teaspoons of water to bind dough.
4.  Chill for 30 minutes.
5.  Pre-heat oven to 180°C.
6.  Roll out the mixture and cut out shapes.
7.  Place on a greased baking sheet and chill for 10-15 minutes.
8.  Bake for 8 minutes.
9.  Cool on wire rack.
10. Decorate the biscuits with coloured icing of your choice.

# Keeping Busy

## Christmas Chains

It's always great fun to make your own decorations. Here are some tips on how to make a Christmas paper chain!

### Here's what you need:
Several sheets of red and green paper
Scissors
Craft glue
Marker pen
Silver and gold glitter

### And here's what you do:

1. Ask an adult to cut 12 strips of red paper and 12 strips of green, making sure they are the same size.
2. Draw a picture in the middle of each strip or glue on a small picture cut out from wrapping paper.
3. Use glue to add glitter to your strip.
4. Then glue the ends of each strip, linking them as you go.

*Adult help needed!*

## Reindeer Prints

Here's a fun and easy way to make your very own reindeer picture.

### Here's what you need:
White or coloured paper
Paint
Pencil
Paintbrush

### And here's what you do:

1. Stand on the paper and trace around one of your feet.
2. Paint this shape brown. This is the reindeer's head.
3. Choose a different colour for the antlers. Dip your hand in this paint and then place one hand on either side of the reindeer's head. Press hard.
4. Do the same again but this time place your hand prints above the first two you made.
5. You can now paint eyes, a nose and a mouth on the reindeer's face.

*Adult help needed!*

# Food for the Reindeer!

Santa's reindeer will be hungry after the long journey so here's a recipe for their favourite food.

## Here's what you need:
A large bowl
Parchment paper
Ribbon or string
Oats
Glitter
Granulated sugar
Cinnamon sticks

## And here's what you do:

1. Mix all the ingredients in a large bowl.
2. Cut the parchment paper into large squares.
3. Place about a tablespoon into each square and scrunch up until you have a little bag. Tie the bag with ribbon or string and leave in a cool place.
4. On Christmas Eve before you go to bed, sprinkle on the lawn or outside your house. The moon and stars will make it shine and lead the reindeer to your house.

*Adult help needed!*

---

# Christmas Stocking

Make a Christmas stocking for your favourite toy!

## Here's what you need:
Thick brown paper or brown felt
Pencil
Scissors
Glue
Hole-punch
Wool
Markers
Glitter
Stickers

## And here's what you do:

1. Ask an adult to cut out two large stocking shapes from the paper or felt.
2. Glue the edges of the stocking together.
3. Punch holes around the edges of the stocking.
4. Knot one end and thread the wool in and out of the holes. Leave enough to make a loop at the top of the stocking.
5. Decorate the stocking with glitter, pictures or stickers.
6. Wrap a little present for your favourite toy and pop it inside.
7. Hang the stocking up on Christmas Eve.

*Adult help needed!*

# Cotton Wool Snowman

Here's how to make your very own snowman.

### Here's what you need:

A cotton wool ball
A roll of cotton wool
A toilet roll tube
Black card
Orange card
Scissors
Craft glue
Coloured wool

## And here's what you do:

1.  Ask an adult to cut lengthways down the toilet roll and curl and glue the edges together to make a cone shape.
2.  To make the snowman's body, wrap and glue the cotton wool around the cone.
3.  For the head, glue the cotton wool ball on top of the body.
4.  To make the hat, eyes, mouth and buttons cut different sized circles and a hat shape from the black card.
5.  Don't forget the snowman's nose! Make a small cone shape from the orange card.
6.  Glue all the card pieces carefully on to the snowman.
7.  Finish off by adding the wool as a scarf.

Adult help needed!

# Learning Fun

# Christmas abc

a
b
c
d
e
f
g
h
i
j
k
l
m
n

Can you name all the pictures?

o p q

r s t

u v w

x Xmas y z

Can you think of any other Christmas words?

# Christmas Numbers

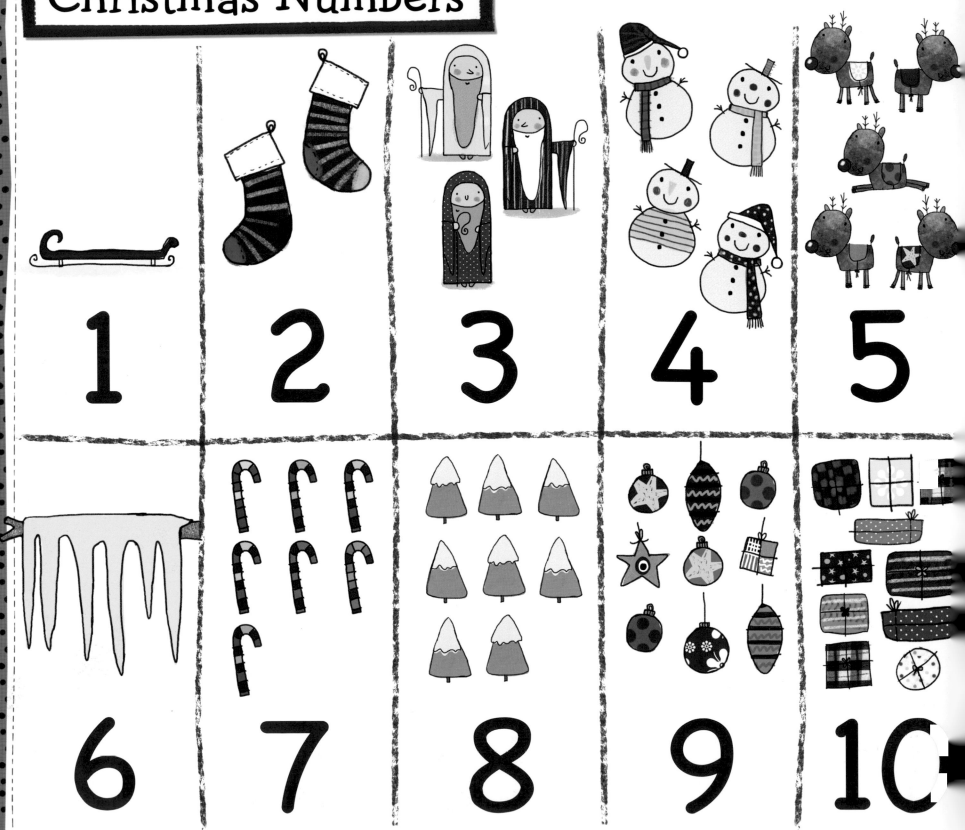

How many reindeer can you count?

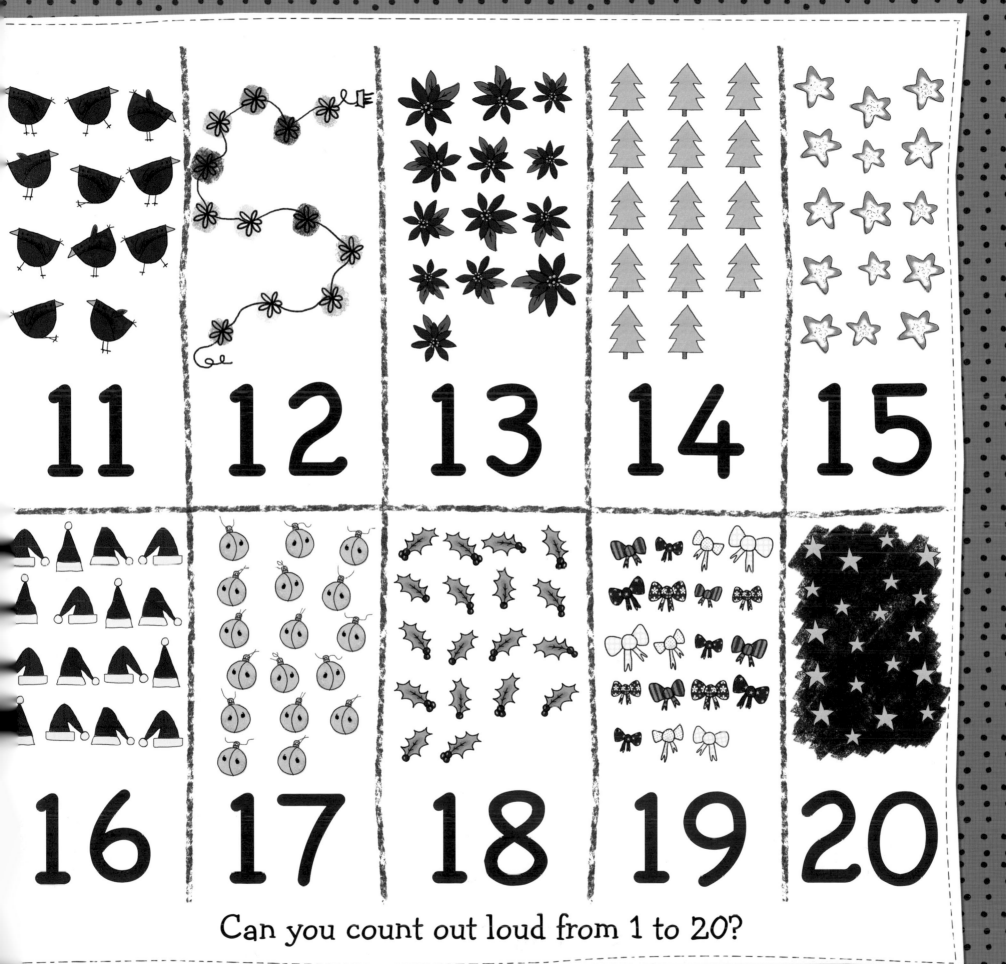

**11  12  13  14  15**

**16  17  18  19  20**

Can you count out loud from 1 to 20?

# Christmas Colours

red      blue      yellow

green      brown      purple

# Christmas Shapes

Can you find these shapes?

# Happy Christmas!

## Yes or No?

Do we send birthday cards at Christmas?
Yes or No?

Does Santa have a long white beard?
Yes or No?

Are Christmas trees yellow?
Yes or No?

Do we hang up a shoe on Christmas Eve?
Yes or No?

Do the fairies leave our Christmas presents?
Yes or No?

Does Santa say "Ho! Ho! Ho!"?
Yes or No?

## Can You Guess?

A snowman wears this.

You put this on the Christmas tree.

You sit on this in the snow.

You eat this at Christmas.

You wear this at Christmas time.

You see this at Christmas.

# Christmas Quiz

## Do You Know?

Who pulls Santa's sleigh?

Where does Santa live?
- The North Pole
- The park
- The jungle

Who helps Santa to make all the presents?

What's the weather like in Santa's home?
- Snowy
- Sunny
- Rainy

What does Santa carry in his sack?

What colour clothes does Santa wear?

## Can You Remember?

Where was the Baby Jesus born?
- Stable
- House
- Park

Who told the shepherds that the Baby Jesus had been born?

How many Wise Men came to visit Baby Jesus?
- 2
- 3
- 4

What did the Wise Men bring the Baby Jesus?

Which animal watched over the Baby Jesus?
- Donkey
- Cat
- Hen

What was in the sky the night the Baby Jesus was born?

As dry leaves that before the wild hurricane fly,
When they meet with an obstacle, mount to the sky.
So up to the house-top the coursers they flew,
With sleigh full of toys, and St Nicholas too.

And then, in a twinkling, I heard on the roof
The prancing and pawing of each little hoof.
As I drew in my head, and was turning around,
Down the chimney St Nicholas came with a bound.

He was dressed all in fur, from his head to his foot,
And his clothes were all tarnished with ashes and soot.
A bundle of toys he had flung on his back,
And he looked like a peddler, just opening his pack.

His eyes, how they twinkled! His dimples, how merry!
His cheeks were like roses, his nose like a cherry!
His droll little mouth was drawn up like a bow,
And the beard on his chin was as white as the snow.

The stump of a pipe he held tight in his teeth,
And the smoke it encircled his head like a wreath.
He had a broad face and a little round belly,
That shook when he laughed like a bowl full of jelly!

He was chubby and plump, a right jolly old elf,
And I laughed when I saw him, in spite of myself!
A wink of his eye and a twist of his head,
Soon gave me to know I had nothing to dread.

He spoke not a word, but went straight to his work,
And filled all the stockings, then turned with a jerk.
And laying his finger aside of his nose,
And giving a nod, up the chimney he rose.

He sprang to his sleigh, to his team gave a whistle,
And away they all flew like the down of a thistle.
But I heard him exclaim as he drove out of sight,
"Merry Christmas to all, and to all a Good Night!"

by Clement C. Moore

# 'Twas The Night Before Christmas

'Twas the night before Christmas, when all through the house
Not a creature was stirring, not even a mouse.
The stockings were hung by the chimney with care,
In hopes that St Nicholas soon would be there.

The children were nestled all snug in their beds,
While visions of sugar-plums danced in their heads.
And mamma in her 'kerchief, and I in my cap,
Had just settled down for a long winter's nap.

When out on the lawn there rose such a clatter,
I sprang from my bed to see what was the matter.
Away to the window I flew like a flash,
Tore open the shutters and threw up the sash.

The moon on the breast of the new-fallen snow,
Gave a lustre of midday to objects below.
When, what to my wondering eyes should appear,
But a miniature sleigh, and eight tiny reindeer.

With a little old driver, so lively and quick,
I knew in a moment it must be St Nick.
More rapid than eagles his coursers they came,
And he whistled, and shouted, and called them by name!

"Now Dasher! Now, Dancer! Now, Prancer and Vixen!
On, Comet! On, Cupid! On, Donder and Blitzen!
To the top of the porch, to the top of the wall!
Now dash away! Dash away! Dash away all!"

Little donkey, little donkey
Had a heavy day.
Little donkey carry Mary
Safely on her way.

Little donkey, little donkey
Journey's end is near.
There are wise men waiting for a
Sign to bring them here.

Do not falter, little donkey
There's a star ahead.
It will guide you, little donkey
To a cattle shed.

Ring out those bells tonight
Bethlehem, Bethlehem.
Follow that star tonight
Bethlehem, Bethlehem.

# Little Donkey

Little donkey, little donkey
On the dusty road.
Got to keep on plodding onwards
With your precious load.

Been a long time, little donkey
Through the winter's night.
Don't give up now, little donkey
Bethlehem's in sight.

Ring out those bells tonight
Bethlehem, Bethlehem.
Follow that star tonight
Bethlehem, Bethlehem.

The Nutcracker raced over to Glara to thank her and the next moment they were floating through the air on a magical sleigh. And as she turned to talk to the Nutcracker, Glara saw he had been changed into a young prince who promised to look after her. Flying high over the mountain tops, their journey took them to the Land of Snow with enchanted forests and dancing snowflakes.

They landed gently in the faraway Land of Sweets. Glara could hardly believe her eyes. Everything was made out of sweets. When they met the Sugar Plum Fairy, Glara told her all about her brave Nutcracker. The Sugar Plum Fairy was so amazed to hear about their adventures, that she invited them to a celebration inside the Candy Castle. Never had Glara seen so many sweets. When the music started, she clapped and cheered as the dancers performed. And as she watched the Sugar Plum Fairy dance so magnificently with a handsome soldier Glara knew she had never been so happy. She did not want the evening to end.

And as the robin tapped on the snowy window, Glara opened her eyes to find it was Christmas morning. She was still lying under the Christmas tree and, clasped tightly in her hand was her little Nutcracker doll.

# The Nutcracker

It was Christmas Eve and Clara and Fritz watched in wonder as their house filled with guests. This was the best party they had ever been to. And when Clara's godfather gave her a beautiful Nutcracker doll, she thought she would burst with excitement. But when Fritz saw Clara's present he was jealous. He snatched the doll and threw it across the floor, breaking it. Clara was heartbroken. Fortunately, her clever godfather was able to fix the Nutcracker and made a little bed for the doll under the Christmas tree. When the dancing had stopped and all the guests had gone, Clara lay down beside the tree and fell fast asleep holding her Nutcracker doll.

She was woken by the sound of a trumpet and amazed when she saw that all the toys around the tree had come to life. Suddenly the room was filled with an army of mice led by the huge Mouse King with seven heads. They had come for a fight. Clara blinked away her sleepiness and saw that her Nutcracker had grown really tall. He was giving orders to his soldier army to stand in a line. Clara held her breath as the brave Nutcracker fought with the evil Mouse King.

But the Mouse King proved to be too strong and Clara could see that the Nutcracker was in danger. Silently she took off her slipper and, aiming straight at the Mouse King, she flung the slipper at his head. In an instant he fell to the floor.

# We Wish You A Merry Christmas

We wish you a Merry Christmas,
We wish you a Merry Christmas,
We wish you a Merry Christmas
And a Happy New Year.

Good tidings we bring
To you and your kin,
Good tidings for Christmas
And a Happy New Year.

Oh, bring us a figgy pudding,
Oh, bring us a figgy pudding,
Oh, bring us a figgy pudding
And a cup of good cheer!

We won't go until we get some,
We won't go until we get some,
We won't go until we get some,
So bring some out here!

We wish you a Merry Christmas,
We wish you a Merry Christmas,
We wish you a Merry Christmas
And a Happy New Year.

# Jingle Bells

Dashing through the snow
In a one horse open sleigh
O'er the fields we go
Laughing all the way.
Bells on bob tails ring
Making spirits bright
What fun it is to laugh and sing
A sleighing song tonight.

Oh, jingle bells, jingle bells
Jingle all the way.
Oh, what fun it is to ride
In a one horse open sleigh.
Jingle bells, jingle bells
Jingle all the way.
Oh, what fun it is to ride
In a one horse open sleigh.

When they saw the bright light shining over an inn, they spoke to the innkeeper. "Has a baby been born?" they asked. The innkeeper told them to go to the stable behind the inn. Inside the shepherds found Mary and Joseph and the Baby Jesus. The Baby Jesus was sleeping in a manger. The shepherds knelt down before the Baby.

In a country far away, three Wise Men saw a bright new star in the sky. They knew the star meant that a very important king was to be born and that he would become King of the Jews. They followed the star all the way to Bethlehem where it stopped above the stable.

"Is there a new king born today?" they asked Mary and Joseph. Mary showed them Baby Jesus. The Wise Men gave him their gifts of gold and frankincense and a special ointment called myrrh.

And on that very first Christmas night as a choir of angels sang in the sky, the Wise Men and the shepherds gave thanks to God. Mary gazed lovingly at her baby son as he slept in the manger.

She knew that a miracle had taken place and that the world would never be the same again.

# The First Christmas

One day an angel came to visit Mary. "Do not be afraid," the angel said, "you will have a son and you will call him Jesus."

Now some time later, Mary and Joseph were told they had to go to Bethlehem. They loaded their donkey with food and water and clothes for the baby. Bethlehem was far away and it was a long, tiring journey. Mary's baby was due very soon and they had to stop many times for Mary to rest.

When they finally reached Bethlehem it was very late. The small town was noisy and crowded. Joseph tried hard to find somewhere for them to stay. But everywhere they went, the reply was the same, "I am sorry we are full."

When they knocked on the door of the last inn, Joseph had little hope. "I am very sorry," said the innkeeper, "we are full." But when he saw how tired Mary was, he suddenly added, "Follow me, I might be able to help." He took Mary and Joseph to the back of the inn. "If you don't mind sleeping with the animals, you can stay here," the innkeeper told them kindly. Mary and Joseph gladly accepted his offer. Inside, Joseph made a bed of straw for Mary to lie on. That night, Mary's baby son was born. She called him Jesus and wrapped him in warm clothes and laid him in the manger.

Up on the hills just outside Bethlehem, shepherds were guarding their sheep. Suddenly a bright light shone in the sky and an angel appeared. "Tonight the Son of God was born in Bethlehem," the angel told them. "Follow the star and you will find the Baby Jesus in a stable." So the shepherds gathered their sheep and set off down the hill into Bethlehem.

# Stories and Songs